MESSIAH

HIGHLIGHTS FROM HANDEL'S ORATORIO AND OTHER CHRISTMAS MUSIC

MESSIAH

HIGHLIGHTS FROM HANDEL'S ORATORIO AND OTHER CHRISTMAS MUSIC

A selection of music by HANDEL, BACH, BERLIOZ, BRITTEN, AND OTHERS

Compiled and edited by DAVID WILLCOCKS

VICTOR GOLLANCZ LTD in association with
The Metropolitan Museum of Art, New York
LONDON 1987

I am grateful for the valuable assistance of
ALDEN ROCKWELL MURPHY
in the preparation of this volume.

Front jacket: *The Annunciation* (detail)
Illuminated manuscript page from the *Belles Heures* of Jean, Duc de Berry,
folio 30
Pol, Jean and Herman de Limbourg, French (Parisian)
Tempera and gold leaf on vellum, ca. 1406–09

The Cloisters Collection, 1954   54.1.1

Back jacket: *Virgin and Child in an Apse* (detail)
Workshop of Robert Campin, Flemish, active by 1406, d. 1444
Oil and tempera on canvas, transferred from wood

Rogers Fund, 1905   05.39.2

First published in Great Britain 1987
by Victor Gollancz Ltd,
14 Henrietta Street, London WC2E 8QJ

Copyright © 1987 by The Metropolitan Museum of Art

Produced by the Department of Special Publications,
The Metropolitan Museum of Art
Designed by Peter Oldenburg
Music engraved by David Budmen, MusicNote, Inc., Pitman, New Jersey
Photography by The Metropolitan Museum of Art Photograph Studio
Printed and bound by A. Mondadori, Verona, Italy

ISBN 0 575 03918 3

TABLE OF CONTENTS

INTRODUCTION

THE STORY OF the Infant Jesus, born of a Virgin Mother and worshipped in a lowly stable by Magi led to Bethlehem by a star, has kindled the imagination of poets, musicians, painters and sculptors for many centuries. Just as some artists have worked on a large scale while others have expressed themselves in miniature, so musicians have responded with works that range from elaborate oratorios to simple carols.

Among the best loved of the large musical works associated with Christmas are George Frideric Handel's *Messiah* (1742), Johann Sebastian Bach's *Christmas Oratorio* (1734), and *L'Enfance du Christ* (1850-1854) by Hector Berlioz. The first part of *Messiah* is devoted to the prophecy of Christ's birth and the fulfilment of that prophecy. Bach's oratorio is a collection of six cantatas to be performed at church services between Christmas and Epiphany. The oratorio by Berlioz describes the flight of the Holy Family into Egypt to escape the wrath of Herod.

Excerpts from these three oratorios are included in this book, as well as a number of carols. Accompanying the music are reproductions of paintings, sculpture and other works from the collections of The Metropolitan Museum of Art in New York City. Like the music, much of this art celebrates the birth and life of Christ.

It is important to note that a difference exists between the art of the painter and the art of the musician. When a painter has finished his work, his picture will be there for posterity. Although it may require periodic restoration or cleaning, the painting will in essence remain as the artist conceived it. A musical composition, on the other hand, has to be translated into sound before it can be fully appreciated, and the composer remains at the mercy of successive generations of performers who may impose upon the work interpretations that differ widely from each other and from the composer's own conception of his creation.

Handel's *Messiah* is performed today in many different ways, ranging from the singing of favourite airs and choruses by a family gathered round a piano, through "authentic" performances with a small chamber choir and instruments of Handel's period, to the mammoth presentations involving several thousand singers, often supported by a correspondingly large modern orchestra using additional instrumental parts written by Mozart. Whenever, wherever, however *Messiah* is performed, Handel's genius is apparent—the genius recognised by Haydn who said, "He is, indeed, the father of us all"; by Mozart who declared, "Handel understands effect better than any of us"; and by Beethoven who confessed, "I would uncover my head to kneel down on his tomb."

Who can read the phrases "Every valley shall be exalted . . . and the glory of the Lord shall be revealed . . . for unto us a child is born" without thinking of Handel's music to which those words seem indissolubly wed? Composers of lesser stature have been accused of naïveté when they have written descriptive music, but Handel's memorable melodic lines spring naturally from the verbal text:

shall be ex - alt - - - - - - ed

the crook - ed__ straight

is ris - en,__ is ris - en__ up - on__ thee,__ is ris - en

Handel's experience as a composer of opera accounts for his ability to provide dramatic music that matches the mood of the words. Examples abound: the vitality and joy of "For unto us a child is born"; the brilliance and splendour of "Glory to God in the highest," with the distant trumpets proclaiming the arrival of the heavenly host and the strings in their final diminuendo suggesting the return of the angels to heaven; the tranquillity of the pastoral "He shall feed his flock"; and not least, the grandeur of the unison "For the Lord God omnipotent reigneth" amid the exultant cries of "Hallelujah!" It was of the "Hallelujah" chorus that Handel is alleged to have said, when composing it, "I thought I saw all heaven before me, and the great God himself."

If Handel (1685-1759) was the exponent *par excellence* of the dramatic in music, his contemporary, J. S. Bach (1685-1750), epitomised the devotional. A feature of Bach's *Christmas Oratorio,* as of his Passion music and many cantatas, is the inclusion of a number of reflective chorales, the melodies of which would have been familiar to Lutheran congregations. Bach's arrangement of these chorales reveals a vivid imagination, sometimes in the colourful orchestration, but more often in the poignant harmonies. In "Ah! dearest Jesus, holy child," three trumpets seem to hover over the cradle like guardian angels, and in "Break forth, O beauteous, heav'nly light" there is brilliance in the part-writing and luminosity in the harmonic texture.

Unlike Bach, Hector Berlioz (1803-1869) was contemptuous of conventional Christianity, but he developed a deep religious instinct, which found expression in his sacred trilogy *L'Enfance du Christ.* "The Shepherds' Farewell," now to be found in the second part of that work, was originally published separately and modestly passed off by the composer as the work of a mythical seventeenth-century musician, Pierre Ducré. Immediately popular, the work has never lost its appeal.

Of the carols included in this book, nearly half are of English origin and described as traditional, because neither the authors of the words nor the composers of the melodies can be identified. These traditional carols have been handed down from generation to generation, so it is not surprising that many versions exist of the words and the tunes.

Benjamin Britten (1913-1976), represented in this book by "A New Year Carol," made a valuable contribution to the repertory of twentieth-century Christmas music. In works such as "A Boy is born" and "A Ceremony of Carols" the influence of plainsong and medieval polyphony can be detected. Although capable of composing ornate and complex music, Britten responded to the anonymous words of "A New Year Carol" with a setting of exquisite simplicity.

The other carols, drawn from French, German, Dutch and Basque sources, reflect the range and rich diversity of the music sung at Christmastide. Some, like "Unto us is born a son" and "Blessed be that maid," employ the macaronic form, in which lines of Latin are interspersed with vigorous vernacular phrases; some, such as "The Cherry Tree Carol," are cast in ballad form—that is, they tell a story; while "The infant King," "A virgin most pure," "King Jesus hath a garden" and "The seven joys of Mary" have a recurring refrain. Common to all the carols, and to the hymn "As with gladness," are directness of expression and clarity of structure.

The paintings reproduced in this book range from the rich, majestic pageantry of such fifteenth-century masters as Hans Memling and Giovanni di Paolo to the ebullience of François Boucher in the eighteenth century. A lively millefleurs tapestry decorates "A New Year Carol" and a delicate polychromed wood sculpture accompanies "The seven joys of Mary." There are many other reproductions of painting and sculpture, as well as examples of stained glass, manuscript illumination, etching, drawing and embroidery.

It is my hope that the contents of this book will be as much a joy to the eye as to the ear.

DAVID WILLCOCKS

A NOTE ON THE MUSIC FOR MESSIAH

In the excerpts from *Messiah* selected for this book, type of normal size has been used for all notes written by Handel, and for his indications of tempo, dynamics and ornamentation. Since he composed at great speed (the first version of *Messiah* was produced in a mere twenty-four days), it is remarkable that he was almost always able to indicate his general intentions. In the cases where, by analogy, additional trills and other notation seem desirable, these have been inserted, but clearly differentiated from Handel's own marks by square brackets [ ] and crossed slurs ⌢ .

The keyboard accompaniment is an almost exact transcription of the original orchestral parts; only rarely has it been necessary to make slight adaptations (generally involving the transposition of one or more notes by an octave) to make the keyboard part easier to play. Handel's accompaniments, particularly of solo airs, sometimes consisted only of a bass line known as the *basso continuo,* it being understood that the keyboard player, often an organist, would provide the necessary additional harmonic support for this line. Continuo players were free to determine the texture and degree of elaboration in their realisations; my own realisation, shown by notes in small type in the accompaniment, is but one example.

DW

8

Highlights from HANDEL'S MESSIAH

EV'RY VALLEY
SHALL BE EXALTED

Isaiah 40:4

G. F. Handel
Tenor solo from *Messiah*

AND THE GLORY OF THE LORD

Isaiah 40:5

G. F. Handel
Chorus from *Messiah*

O THOU THAT TELLEST GOOD TIDINGS

Isaiah 40:9
60:1

G. F. Handel
Alto solo from *Messiah*

ti-dings to Zi - on,　　　　　　　　　　get thee up　in - to the high moun - tain,

O THOU THAT TELLEST GOOD TIDINGS

un- to the ci - ties of Ju - - dah, Be - hold_____ your God!_____ be -

hold your God!_____ be - hold your God!

O thou that tell-est good ti-dings to Zi - on,   a -

rise, shine; for thy light is come,   a - rise,__ a -

D. C. (to page 30)

FOR UNTO US
A CHILD IS BORN

G. F. Handel

Chorus from *Messiah*

Isaiah 9:6

GLORY TO GOD
IN THE HIGHEST

Luke 2:14

G. F. Handel
Chorus from *Messiah*

Glo - ry to God, glo - ry to God in the high - - est, and peace on earth,

Glo - ry to God, glo - ry to God, glo - ry to God in the

high - est, and peace on earth,

HE SHALL FEED HIS FLOCK

Isaiah 40:11
Matthew 11:28-29

G. F. Handel
Alto and Soprano solos from *Messiah*

Larghetto e piano

Alto

He shall— feed his flock like a shep – – herd: and

he — shall — ga - ther the lambs— with — his arm, with — his — arm.

eus in ad
iutorium
meum t
intende.

Domine ad adiu
uandum me festia.
Gloria pri et filio
et spiritui sancto.

He shall___ feed his flock like a shep - - herd: and

he___ shall___ ga - ther the lambs___ with___ his arm, with ___ his ___ arm,

and car - ry___ them___ in his bo - som, and

un - to____ him,____ all ye that la - bor, come un - to____ him, that

are____ hea - vy la - den,____ and he__ will give__ you rest.

Take his yoke up-on you, and learn___ of him; for he___ is___ meek___ and

low - ly of heart:___ and ye___ shall find rest,___ and ye shall find rest___ un -

to___ your souls, take his yoke up-on you, and

learn____ of him; for he____ is____ meek____ and low - ly of heart:____ and

ye____ shall find rest,____ and ye shall find rest____ un - to____ your souls.

HALLELUJAH

Revelation 19:6
11:15
19:16

G. F. Handel
Chorus from *Messiah*

et dicebant quia hic est saluator

Selections from CHRISTMAS ORATORIOS
AND OTHER HOLIDAY MUSIC

AH! DEAREST JESUS, HOLY CHILD

J. S. Bach
from the *Christmas Oratorio*

Translated by
the Reverend John Troutbeck

Ah! dear - est Je - sus,— ho - ly child,

BREAK FORTH, O BEAUTEOUS, HEAV'NLY LIGHT

Translated by
the Reverend John Troutbeck

J. S. Bach
from the *Christmas Oratorio*

Break— forth,— O beau - teous,— heav'n - ly light, And— ush - er— in— the— morn — ing;
Ye— shep - herds, shrink— not — with— af - fright, But— hear— the an - gel's— warn — ing.

This— child,— now weak— in in - fan - cy, Our— con - fi - dence— and— joy— shall be,

The— pow'r of— Sa - tan— break — ing, Our— peace— e - ter - nal— mak — ing.

A NEW YEAR CAROL

Words anonymous.

Benjamin Britten

Quietly

pp

% *p*

1. Here we bring new wa - ter from the
2. Sing _ reign of Fair _ Maid, with
3. Sing _ reign of Fair _ Maid, with

3rd verse to ⊕

(v. 3 ———)

well _ so clear,   For to wor-ship God with, this hap - py New Year.
gold up-on her toe,   O-pen you the West Door, and turn the Old Year go.
gold up-on her chin,   O-pen you the East Door, and let the New Year in.

Sing

(v. 3 ———)

THE SHEPHERDS' FAREWELL

Translated by Paul England

Hector Berlioz
from *L'Enfance du Christ*
(slightly adapted)

Allegretto

1. Thou__ must leave thy__ low - ly
2. Bless - ed Je - sus,__ we__ im -
3. Blest__ are ye be - yond__ all

dwell - ing, The hum - ble crib, the sta - ble bare, Babe, all mor - tal
plore thee, With hum - ble love and ho - ly fear, In the land that
mea - sure, Thou hap - py fa - ther, mo - ther mild! Guard ye well your

poco **f**

babes__ ex - cell - ing, Con - tent__ our earth - ly lot__ to share.
lies __ be - fore thee, For - get__ not us__ who lin - ger here!
heav'n - ly trea - sure, The Prince__ of Peace,__ the Ho - ly Child!

* Small notes are alternatives for 1st and 2nd basses.

Loving father, loving mother, Shelter thee with
May the shepherd's lowly calling, Ever to thy
God go with you, God protect you, Guide you safely

tender care! Loving father, loving mother,
heart be dear! May the shepherd's lowly calling,
through the wild! God go with you, God protect you,

Shelter thee with tender care, shelter thee with
Ever to thy heart be dear, ever to thy
Guide you safely through the wild, guide you safely

D.C. for verses 2, 3   CODA

tender care!
heart be dear!
through the wild!

BLESSED BE THAT MAID

Words by George R. Woodward

English traditional

1. Bless-ed be_ that maid Ma-rie;___ Born_ he was_ of_
2. In a man-ger of an ass ___ Je - su lay_ and_

her_ bo_ dy; Ve - ry_ God_ ere_ time_ be - gan,___
lull - ed_ was; Born_ to die up - on_ the_ tree ___

REFRAIN

Born_ in_ time_ the_ Son_ of_ Man.
Pro - pec - can - te ho - mi - ne. ___ E - ya!_ Je - sus

ho - di - e ___ Na - tus_ est_ de_ vir - gi - ne.

3. Sweet and blissful was the song
   Chanted of the angel throng,
   "Peace on earth," Alleluya.
   In excelsis gloria.
     Eya!, etc.

4. Fare three kings from far-off land,
   Incense, gold, and myrrh in hand;
   In Bethlem the babe they see,
   Stellae ducti lumine.
     Eya!, etc.

5. Make we merry on this fest,
   In quo Christus natus est;
   On this child I pray you call
   To assoil and save us all.
     Eya!, etc.

97

KING JESUS HATH A GARDEN

Translated by George R. Woodward

Dutch traditional

1. King Je - sus hath a gar - den full of di - vers flow'rs, Where I go cull - ing
2. The li - ly, white in blos - som there, is cha - sti - ty: The vi - o - let, with

po - sies gay, all times and hours.
sweet per - fume, hu - mi - li - ty.

REFRAIN

There naught is heard but pa - ra - dise bird, Harp,

With cym - bal,____

dul-ci-mer, lute, With_ cym - bal, trump, and tym - bal, And the ten - der, sooth-ing_ flute;

cym - bal,____

With cym - bal, trump,_ and tym - bal, And the ten - der, sooth-ing_ flute.____

3. The bonny damask-rose is known as patïence:
   The blithe and thrifty marygold, obedïence.

   There naught is heard, etc.

4. The crown imperial bloometh too in yonder place,
   'Tis charity, of stock divine, the flower of grace.

   There naught is heard, etc.

5. Yet, 'mid the brave, the bravest prize of all may claim
   The star of Bethlem—Jesus—blessèd be his name!

   There naught is heard, etc.

6. Ah! Jesu Lord, my heal and weal, my bliss complete,
   Make thou my heart thy garden plot—fair, trim, and neat.

   That I may hear this musick clear:
   Harp, dulcimer, lute,
   With cymbal, trump, and tymbal,
   And the tender, soothing flute.

A VIRGIN MOST PURE

English traditional

1. A___ Vir - gin___ most___ pure as the pro - phets do tell, Hath___ brought___ forth___ a___
2. In___ Beth - le - hem___ Jew - ry a ci - ty there was, Where___ Jo ___ seph ___ and___
3. Then___ they___ were___ con - strain'd in a sta - ble to lie, Where___ hor - ses___ and___
4. Then___ pre - sent - ly___ af - ter the shep - herds did spy A ___ num - ber of___

ba - by, as it hath be - fell; To___ be our Re - deem - er from___ death,___ hell,___ and
Ma - ry to - ge - ther did pass, And___ there to be tax - ed with___ ma - ny one
ass - es they used for to tie; Their___ lodg - ing so___ sim - ple they took___ it no
an - gels that stood in the sky; They___ joy - ful - ly___ talk - ed and___ sweet - ly___ did

sin, Which___ A - dam's trans - gres - sion had wrap - ped us in.
mo, For___ Cae - sar com - mand - ed the same should be so.
scorn, But a - gainst___ the___ next morn - ing our Sa - vior was born.
sing, "To___ God___ be___ all___ glo - ry our hea - ven - ly King."

For refrain, please turn the next page.

Aye, and there - fore_ be_ mer - ry; Re -

joice,_ and be_ you mer - ry; Set_

sor - row_ a - side; Christ_ Je - sus_ our_

Sa - vior was born at_ this tide.

UNTO US IS BORN A SON

Translated by George R. Woodward

Tune from *Piae Cantiones*, 1582

1. Un-to us is born a son, King of quires su-per—nal: See on earth his
2. Christ, from heav'n de-scend-ing low, Comes on earth a stran—ger; Ox and ass their

life be-gun, Of lords the Lord e-ter—nal, Of lords the Lord e-ter—nal.
own-er know, Be-cra-dled in the man—ger, Be-cra-dled in the_ man—ger.

3. This did Herod sore affray,
   And grievously bewilder,
   So he gave the word to slay,
   And slew the little childer,
   And slew the little childer.

4. Of his love and mercy mild
   This the Christmas story;
   And O that Mary's gentle child
   Might lead us up to glory,
   Might lead us up to glory.

5. O and A, and A and O,
   Cum cantibus in choro,
   Let our merry organ go,
   Benedicamus Domino,
   Benedicamus Domino.

THE INFANT KING

Words by Sabine Baring-Gould

Basque noël

1. Lul - la - by ba - by, now re - clin - ing,
2. Lul - la - by ba - by, now a - sleep - ing, *Sing lul - la - by!*
3. Lul - la - by ba - by, now a - doz - ing,
4. Lul - la - by! is the babe a - wak - ing?

Sing lul - la - by!

Hush, do not wake the In - fant King. An - gels are watch - ing, stars are
Hush, do not wake the In - fant King. Soon will come sor - row with the
Hush, do not wake the In - fant King. Soon comes the cross, the nails, the
Hush, do not stir the In - fant King, Dream-ing of Eas - ter, glad - some

Sing lul - la - by!

shin - ing, O - ver the place where he is ly - ing:
morn - ing, Soon will come bit - ter grief and weep - ing:
pierc - ing, Then in the grave at last re - pos - ing:
morn - ing, Con - quer - ing death, its bond - age break - ing:

Sing lul - la - by!

THE INFANT KING   105

IN DULCI JUBILO

Translated by Robert Lucas Pearsall

German traditional

1. In dul - ci ju - bi - lo Let us our hom-age shew;
2. O Je - su par - vu - le, I yearn for thee al - way,

Our heart's joy re - clin - eth In prae - se - pi - o, And
Hear me, I be - seech thee, O Puer op - ti - me, My

like a bright star shin - eth, Ma - tris in gre - mi - o.
pray - er let it reach thee, O Prin - ceps glo - ri - ae.

Al - pha es et O! Al - pha es et O!
Tra - he me post te! Tra - he me post te!

3. *O* | *Patris cari* | *tas!*
   O | *Nati leni* | *tas!*
   | Deeply were we | staínèd
   Per | *nostra crimi* | *na;*

But | thou hast for us | gaínèd
Coe | *lorum gaudi* | *a.*
| O that we were | there,
| O that we were | there!

4. *U* | *bi sunt gaudi* | *a,*
   If | that they be not | there?
   | There are angels | singing
   | *Nova canti* | *ca,*

| There the bells are | ringing
In | *regis curi* | *a.*
| O that we were | there,
| O that we were | there!

* Vertical lines indicate bar lines; strong beat follows bar line.

HE IS BORN THE DIVINE CHRIST CHILD
IL EST NE LE DIVIN ENFANT

Translated by David Willcocks

French traditional

1. More than four thou-sand years on earth, Man a - wait - ed this joy - ous birth.
3. In a man - ger thou deignst to be, For a God, what hu - mi - li - ty!

D.S.

1. De - puis plus de qua - tre mille ans Nous at - ten - dions cet heur - eux temps.
3. Une é - ta - ble est son lo - ge - ment, Pour un Dieu quel a - bais - se - ment!

2. O what beau - ty and charm are thine, Heav'n - ly grace to our hearts sup - ply - ing;
4. Je - su, King, whom we bow be - fore, Yet an in - fant, all power de - ny - ing;

Sop.

Alto

2. Ah! qu'il est beau, qu'il __ est char - mant, Ah! que ses grâ - ces __ sont par - fai - tes;
4. O Jé - sus, roi __ tout puis - sant, Si pe - tit en - fant __ que vous ê - tes;

2. O what beau - ty and charm are thine, O what sweet - ness thou Child di - vine!
4. Je - su, King, whom we bow be - fore, Rule our hearts now and ev - er - more.

D.S.

2. Ah! qu'il est beau, qu'il __ est char - mant, Qu'il est doux ce di - vin en - fant!
4. O Jé - sus, roi __ tout puis - sant, Rég - nez sur nous en - tiè - re - ment.

THE SEVEN JOYS OF MARY

English traditional

Sopranos

1. The first good joy that Ma - ry had, It was the joy of one; ___

All

To see the bless - ed Je - sus Christ, When he was first ___ her son: ___

When he was first ___ her son, good Lord; ___ And bless - ed may he be: ___

REFRAIN

Praise ___ Fa - ther, Son, and Ho - ly Ghost To all e - ter - ni - ty. ___

2. The next good joy that Mary had,
   It was the joy of two;
   To see her own son Jesus Christ
   Making the lame to go:
   Making the lame to go, good Lord,
   And happy may we be:
   Praise Father, etc.

3. The next good joy that Mary had,
   It was the joy of three;
   To see her own son Jesus Christ
   Making the blind to see:
   Making the blind to see, good Lord,
   And happy may we be:
   Praise Father, etc.

4. The next good joy that Mary had,
   It was the joy of four;
   To see her own son Jesus Christ
   Reading the bible o'er:
   Reading the bible o'er, good Lord,
   And happy may we be:
   Praise Father, etc.

5. The next good joy that Mary had,
   It was the joy of five;
   To see her own son Jesus Christ
   Bringing the dead alive:
   Bringing the dead alive, good Lord,
   And happy may we be:
   Praise Father, etc.

6. The next good joy that Mary had,
   It was the joy of six;
   To see her own son Jesus Christ
   Upon the crucifix:
   Upon the crucifix, good Lord,
   And happy may we be:
   Praise Father, etc.

7. The next good joy that Mary had,
   It was the joy of seven;
   To see her own son Jesus Christ
   Ascending into heaven:
   Ascending into heaven, good Lord,
   And happy may we be:
   Praise Father, etc.

AS WITH GLADNESS

Words by William Chatterton Dix

Abridged from a chorale by
Conrad Kocher

3. As they offered gifts most rare
   At that manger rude and bare,
   So may we with holy joy,
   Pure, and free from sin's alloy,
   All our costliest treasures bring,
   Christ, to thee our heav'nly King.

4. Holy Jesu, every day
   Keep us in the narrow way;
   And, when earthly things are past,
   Bring our ransomed souls at last
   Where they need no star to guide,
   Where no clouds thy glory hide.

5. In the heav'nly country bright
   Need they no created light;
   Thou its light, its joy, its crown,
   Thou its sun which goes not down:
   There forever may we sing
   Alleluyas to our King.

TOMORROW
SHALL BE MY DANCING DAY

English traditional

1. To - mor-row shall be ___ my danc - ing day; I would ___ my true ___ love did ___ so chance To ___
2. Then was ___ I born of a Vir - gin pure, Of her ___ I took ___ flesh - ly ___ sub - stance, Thus ___
3. In a man - ger laid ___ and wrapp'd ___ I was, So ve - ry poor, ___ this was ___ my chance, Be -

REFRAIN

see the le - gend of ___ my play, To call ___ my true ___ love to ___ my dance.
was I knit ___ to man's ___ na - ture, To call ___ my true ___ love to ___ my dance. *Sing oh! my ___*
twixt an ox and a sil - ly poor ass, To call ___ my true ___ love to ___ my dance.

To ___ see the
Thus ___ was I
Be - twixt an

love, oh! ___ my love, my love, my

love; This ___ have I done ___ for my ___ true love.

114

THE CHERRY TREE CAROL

English traditional

1. When Jo-seph was an old__ man, an old__ man__ was
2. Jo-seph and__ Ma-ry walk'd through an or-chard

he, He__ mar-ried Vir-gin Ma-ry, the__
green, There were ber-ries and__ cher-ries as__

Queen__ of Ga-li__ lee, He__ mar-ried Vir-gin
thick__ as may be seen, There were ber-ries and__

Ma-ry,__ the Queen__ of Ga-li__ lee.
cher-ries__ as thick__ as may be seen.

3. And | Mary spoke to | Joseph,
So | meek and so | mild,
"Joseph, | gather me some | cherries,
For | I am with | child,
Joseph, | gather me some | cherries,
For | I am with | child."

4. And | Joseph flew in | anger,
In | anger flew | he,
"Let the | father of the | baby
Gather | cherries for | thee,
Let the | father of the | baby
Gather | cherries for | thee."

5. Then | up spoke baby | Jesus
From | in Mary's womb,
"Bend | down the tallest | tree
That my | mother might have | some,
Bend | down the tallest | tree
That my | mother might have | some."

6. And | bent down the tallest | branch
Till it | touched Mary's | hand,
Cried | she, "Oh, look thou | Joseph,
I have | cherries by com|mand,"
Cried | she, "Oh, look thou | Joseph,
I have | cherries by com|mand."

* Vertical lines indicate bar lines; strong beat follows bar line.

LIST OF ILLUSTRATIONS

Page 38: *The Annunciation* (detail)
Albrecht Dürer, German, 1471-1528
Woodcut, 1511

Rogers Fund, 1918   18.65.16

Page 39: *Virgin and Child*
Initial "S" from a manuscript illumination
Probably a follower of Stefano da Zevio,
   Italian (Veronese)
Ink, tempera, and gold leaf on vellum,
   ca. 1425

Rogers Fund, 1912   12.56.2

Page 40: Decorative border
Detail (top border) of an illuminated
   manuscript page depicting *The
   Annunciation,* from the *Belles Heures* of
   Jean, Duc de Berry, folio 30
Pol, Jean, and Herman de Limbourg, French
   (Parisian)
Tempera and gold leaf on vellum, ca. 1406-09

The Cloisters Collection, 1954   54.1.1

Pages 42, 43: Decorative borders
Detail from a page of the *Horae in Laudem
   Beatissimae Virginis Mariae, ad usum
   Romanum*
Paris: Simon Colines, 1543

Harris Brisbane Dick Fund, 1924   24.49.10

Page 45: *The Adoration of the Magi*
Quentin Massys, Flemish, 1465/66-1530
Tempera and oil on wood, 1526

John Stewart Kennedy Fund, 1911   11.143

Pages 46, 47: Decorative borders
Detail (side border) of an illuminated
   manuscript page depicting *The Flight into
   Egypt,* from the *Belles Heures* of Jean,
   Duc de Berry, folio 63
Pol, Jean, and Herman de Limbourg, French
   (Parisian)
Tempera and gold leaf on vellum, ca. 1406-09

The Cloisters Collection, 1954   54.1.1

Page 49: *Two Winged Putti*
François Boucher, French, 1703-1770
Black chalk and gray wash, heightened with
   white, on beige paper

Gift of Charles K. Lock, 1960   60.175.1

Page 52: *Angel, The Annunciation,* and *The
   Nativity*
Detail of a reliquary shrine of the Virgin and
   Child, believed made for Queen Elizabeth
   of Hungary
French (possibly Parisian), ca. 1340
Silver gilt and translucent enamel

The Cloisters Collection, 1962   62.96

Page 55: *Madonna and Child with Angels*
Pietro di Domenico da Montepulciano,
   Italian (School of the Marches), active first
   quarter 15th century
Tempera on wood, gold ground

Rogers Fund, 1907   07.201

Page 56: *Madonna and Child Enthroned, with
   Saints*
Raphael, Italian (Umbrian), 1483-1520
Tempera, oil, and gold on wood

Gift of J. Pierpont Morgan, 1916   16.30a,b

Page 57: God the Father
Detail from *The Annunciation*
Martin Schongauer, German, 1450(?)-1491
Engraving, ca. 1484

Harris Brisbane Dick Fund, 1932   32.64.1

Page 58: Palmette and rosette border
Pot-metal glass
French (possibly Abbey of St.-Rémy at
   Reims), ca. 1200

The Cloisters Collection, 1978   1978.408.2

Page 59: Hand of God with two censing
   angels
Plaque from a châsse
North Spanish, late 11th century
Champlevé enamel on copper gilt

Gift of J. Pierpont Morgan, 1917   17.190.687

Pages 60, 61: Decorative borders
Detail (bottom border) of an illuminated page
   from a choir book
Italian (probably Florentine), mid-15th
   century
Tempera and gold leaf on parchment

Gift of Louis L. Lorillard, 1896   96.32.16

Page 62: *Heavenly Host*
Detail of an illuminated manuscript page
   from the *Belles Heures* of Jean, Duc de Berry,
   folio 218
Pol, Jean, and Herman de Limbourg, French
   (Parisian)
Ink, tempera, and gold leaf on vellum,
   ca. 1406-09

The Cloisters Collection, 1954   54.1.1

Page 63: *Infant Joy* (detail)
Page from *Songs of Innocence and Experience,*
   1794 (1825 printing)
William Blake, British, 1757-1827
Relief etching, hand-painted with watercolor
   and gold

Rogers Fund, 1917   17.10.25

Page 64: *The Adoration of the Magi*
Illuminated manuscript page from the *Belles
   Heures* of Jean, Duc de Berry, folio 54v
Pol, Jean, and Herman de Limbourg, French
   (Parisian)
Ink, tempera, and gold leaf on vellum,
   ca. 1406-09

The Cloisters Collection, 1954   54.1.1

Page 65: Decorative border
Detail from a page of the *Horae in Laudem
   Beatissimae Virginis Mariae, ad usum
   Romanum*
Paris: Simon Colines, 1543

Harris Brisbane Dick Fund, 1924   24.49.10

Page 66: *Angel with a Banderole*
Camillo Procaccini, Italian, ca. 1555-1629
Red chalk and red wash, heightened with
   white, on beige paper

Harry G. Sperling Fund, 1976   1976.186

Page 67: *God the Father and Angels Adoring the
   Christ Child*
Giovanni Benedetto Castiglione, Italian,
   1609-1670
Etching
Purchase, Joseph Pulitzer Bequest, 1917   17.50.17(48)

Page 68: *Virgin and Child with the Cat; and
   Joseph at the Window*
Rembrandt, Dutch, 1606-1669
Etching, 1654

Purchase, Gift of Henry Walters, by exchange, 1923
23.51.5

Page 69: Decorative border
Detail (side border) of an illuminated
   manuscript page depicting the *Heavenly
   Host,* from the *Belles Heures* of Jean,
   Duc de Berry, folio 218
Pol, Jean, and Herman de Limbourg, French
   (Parisian)
Tempera and gold leaf on vellum, ca. 1406-09

The Cloisters Collection, 1954   54.1.1

Page 70: *Virgin and Child*
Attributed to Claux de Werve, French
   (Burgundian)
From the Convent of the Poor Clares, Poligny
Polychromed and gilded limestone,
   ca. 1415-17

Rogers Fund, 1933   33.23

Page 104: *The Nativity*
Lorenzo Monaco, Italian (Florentine),
   b. ca. 1370, d. 1425
Tempera on wood, gold ground

Robert Lehman Collection, 1975   1975.1.66

Page 105: Decorative borders
Details from a page of the *Horae in Laudem
   Beatissimae Virginis Mariae, ad usum
   Romanum*
Paris: Simon Colines, 1543

Harris Brisbane Dick Fund, 1924   24.49.10

Page 107: *Madonna and Child in a Niche*
Luca della Robbia, Italian (Florentine),
   1399/1400-1482
Enameled terra-cotta

Bequest of Susan Dwight Bliss, 1966   67.55.98

Page 109: *The Nativity*
Workshop of Fra Angelico, Italian
   (Florentine)
Tempera and gold on wood, ca. second quarter
   15th century

Gift of May Dougherty King, 1983   1983.490

Page 110: Decorative border
Detail (bottom border) of an illuminated page
   from a choir book
Attributed to Francesco d'Antonio del Cherico
   and associates, Italian (Florentine)
Tempera and gold leaf on parchment, third
   quarter 15th century

Gift of Louis L. Lorillard, 1896   96.32.8

Page 111: *Virgin and Child*
German (Rhenish or Bohemian), first quarter
   15th century
Polychromed and gilded wood

Anonymous Loan

Page 113: *The Nativity and
   the Annunciation to the Magi*
Detail from the central panel of *The Nativity*
   altarpiece
Workshop of Rogier van der Weyden,
   Flemish, b. 1399/1400, d. 1464
Tempera and oil on wood

The Cloisters Collection, 1949   49.109

Page 114: *Virgin and Child*
German, 15th century
Hand-colored woodcut

Gift of Felix M. Warburg and his family, 1941   41.1.40

Page 115: *Holy Family*
South German (School of Ulm), ca. 1500
From the church at Gutenzell, Oberamt
   Biberach, Württemberg
Polychromed and gilded wood

Gift of Alastair B. Martin, 1948   48.154.1

Page 120: *Angel with Trumpets*
Luca Cambiaso, Italian (Genoese), 1527-1585
Pen and bistre

Robert Lehman Collection, 1975   1975.1.283

Endleaves: *Dante and Beatrice with the Blessed
   Souls*
Woodcut from *Comedia dell'Inferno, del
   Purgatorio, & del Paradiso*
Canto 27 of *Paradiso,* by Dante Alighieri
Venice: Published by Giovambattista Marchiò
   Sessa et Fratelli, 1578

Gift of Francis Leonard Cater, 1958   58.584

Cover stamping: Trumpeter
Ornamental design from *Daniel's Copy-Book*
London: 1664

Harris Brisbane Dick Fund, 1942   42.69.2

INDEX OF FIRST LINES